MW01077875

My Day With Grandma
Copyright © 2021 Reesa Shayne
All rights reserved.

Print ISBN: 978-1-7370601-0-9
Ebook ISBN: 978-1-7370601-1-6
Mobi ISBN: 978-1-7370601-2-3

This book or any portion thereof may not be reproduced or used in any manner whatsoever without the express written permission of the author and publisher of the book except for brief use of quotations in a book review. For permission requests, write to the author, addressed "Attention: Permissions" at reesashayne@gmail.com. This is a work of fiction. Any resemblance to actual events or persons, living or dead, is entirely coincidental.

Reesa Shayne Books
www.reesashaynebooks.com

Ordering Information:
For details contact reesashayne@gmail.com

Written by Reesa Shayne
Illustrated by: Juanita Taylor

For my incredible nephew Noah.

His love for his grandmother is the inspiration for this story.

And to all grandparents & grandchildren everywhere in the world:

Your love is beautiful.

It is just me
and Grandma
together all
day.

I am excited!

We are going
to play!

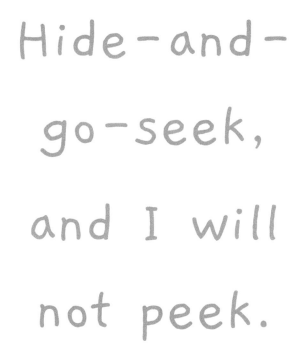

Hide-and-go-seek, and I will not peek.

Then we will
read a book
in the reading
nook.

And we might
go for a walk

with some

sidewalk chalk.

10

For sure we will munch on something yummy for lunch.

We might
even dance
in our jazzy
pants!

And sing a
fun tune
about the
month of
June.

It will be fun
all day
with Grandma
today.

I never want the day to end. She is my best friend.

When it is
time to say
goodbye,
I will try not
to cry.

Because I will see her again soon and be over the moon!

To spend a
full day
with
Grandma
and play...

...All over again, she is my best friend.

The End